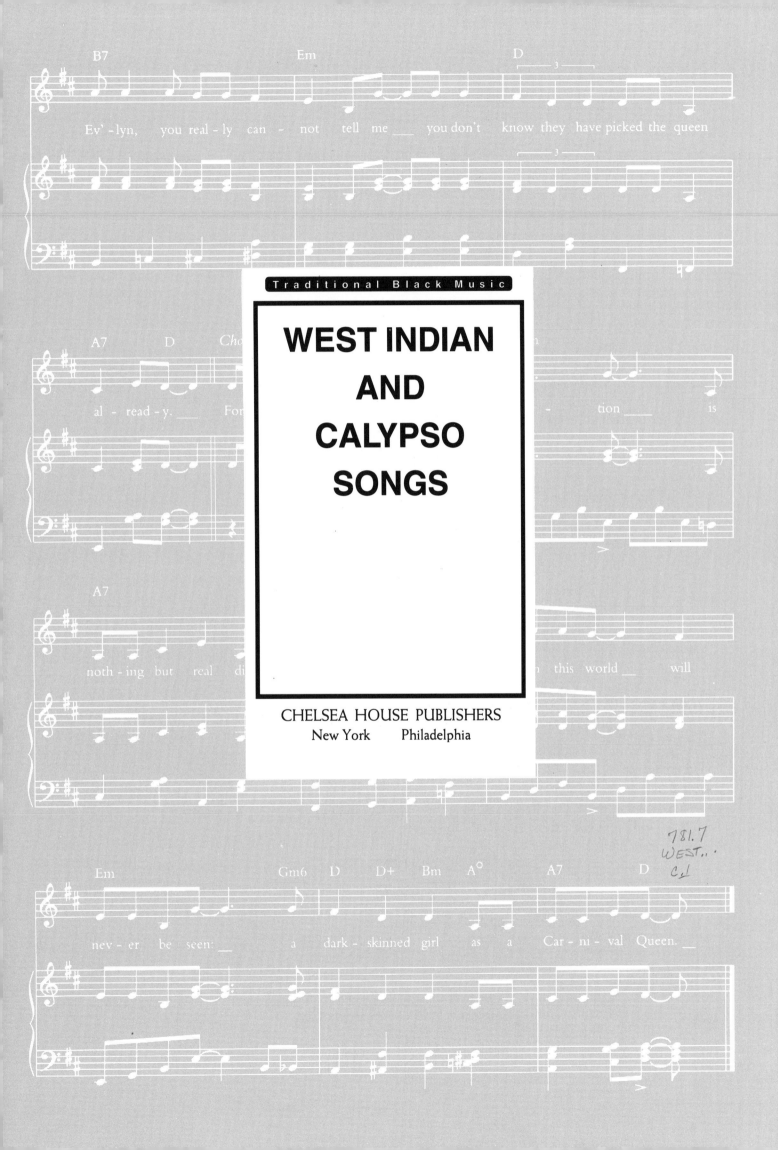

On the cover Dressed in a straw hat, beads, and a colorful blouse, a West Indian girl plays the steel drum in a local parade.

Chelsea House Publishers
Editorial Director Richard Rennert
Executive Managing Editor Karyn Gullen Browne
Copy Chief Robin James
Picture Editor Adrian G. Allen
Art Director Robert Mitchell
Manufacturing Director Gerald Levine

Staff for West Indian and Calypso Songs
Text Editor David Shirley
Copy Editor Joy Sanchez
Editorial Assistant Kelsey Goss
Picture Researcher Villette Harris
Book Layout Jesse Cohen, John Infantino

First Printing
1 3 5 7 9 8 6 4 2

Library of Congress Cataloging-in-Publication Data

West Indian and Calypso songs / [compiled by] Jerry Silverman
1 score. — (Traditional Black music)
Includes index.
  0-7910-1840-7.   0-7910-1856-3 (pbk.)
1. Calypso (Music)—West Indies. I. Silverman, Jerry. II. Series.
M1681.A1W47 1994
                                              93-48056
                                              CIP   M

PICTURE CREDITS
AP/Wide World Photos: pp. 27, 31, 37, 47; The Bettmann Archive: pp. 7, 10, 21, 53, 55; © Katrina Thomas: cover; UPI/Bettmann: pp. 5, 15, 41, 59, 63.

CONTENTS

Author's Preface

The European settlers who conquered the tiny islands of the West Indies during the 16th and 17th centuries brought with them a rich assortment of customs and folkways. Over the years, these new customs were adapted by West African slaves to form a colorful way of life that was totally unique to the islands of the Caribbean.

No other aspect of this new form of cultural expression was as exciting as its music. Blending the complex rhythms of West Africa with the harmonies of European music, the islanders created a style of composition and performance that was both striking and original. The islands' earliest songs were called carisos. These lively songs were first sung on the island of Trinidad during the 18th and early 19th centuries. They contained many words from the Creole language—a unique blend of French, Spanish, and African languages—and described the tropical island paradise through the eyes of the poor and oppressed.

From the beginning, cariso composers have made the best of the islands' multilingual history. The songs often use elaborate rhyme schemes that borrow freely from the vocabularies and speech styles of the islands' various traditions. The predominance of long, polysyllabic words often results in song lyrics that are musical even before the highly syncopated rhythms are added. By placing the "ac-*cent* on the wrong syl-*lable*," the singers give the music its lively, humorous feel.

The songs of cariso eventually evolved into the contemporary songs of carnival or "calypso." These spirited songs comment wittily, often bitingly, on all the pleasures and tribulations of life: politics, religion, sex, discrimination. No topic is left untreated.

Humor plays a large role in calypso music, but it is humor with a cutting edge. In many songs, calypso singers make fun of their oppressors, laughing aloud at the silly customs and ridiculous pretensions of the ruling class. In others, performers use humor to conceal their own anger and pain—"laughing to keep from crying," in the words of the old blues singers of the Mississippi Delta.

From a strictly musical point of view, however, these songs can not fail to delight listeners and performers alike. Whether they are sung in English, Creole, or some other combination of languages, they all tell an interesting and original story.

Jerry Silverman

The Contribution of Blacks to American Art and Culture

Kenneth B. Clark

Historical and contemporary social inequalities have obscured the major contribution of American blacks to American culture. The historical reality of slavery and the combined racial isolation, segregation, and sustained educational inferiority have had deleterious effects. As related pervasive social problems determine and influence the art that any group can not only experience, but also, ironically, the extent to which they can eventually contribute to the society as a whole, this tenet is even more visible when assessing the contributions made by African Americans.

All aspects of the arts have been pursued by black Americans, but music provides a special insight into the persistent and inescapable social forces to which black Americans have been subjected. One can speculate that in their preslavery patterns of life in Africa, blacks used rhythm, melody, and lyrics to hold on to reality, hope, and the acceptance of life. Later, in America, music helped blacks endure the cruelties of slavery. Spirituals and gospel music provided a medium for both communion and communication. As the black experience in America became more complex, so too did black music, which has grown and ramified, dramatically affecting the development of American music in general. The result is that today, more than ever before, black music provides a powerful lens through which we may view the history of black Americans in a new and revealing way.

A Jamaican musician plays the marimba in a local calypso band. The odd assortment of African and European instruments gives calypso music its distinctive sound.

This is a Creole *counjaille* song, first sung by slaves on the French plantations of Louisiana. The dances and dance songs of the Creole slaves were quite different from those of their northern counterparts. Apart from the obvious difference in language, the Creole songs were also less restrained than the songs of slaves in other parts of the country. Many of the lively tunes were driven by drums and other percussion instruments.

AURORE PRADÈRE

pas man -dé sou - liers prin -elle　c'est li mo 'ou - lé c'est li ma pren.
does not want pru - nel -la shoes,　It's her that I want, it's her I'll have.

Ya moun qui dit li trop zolie;
Ya moun qui dit li pas polie;
Tout ça ya dit bin fou bin –
C'est li mo oulé, c'est li ma pren.　*Chorus*

There's some that say that she's too pretty;
There's some that say she's not polite;
All this they say – I'm crazy too –
It's her that I want, it's her I'll have.　*Chorus*

With their simple but colorful peasant dress, the women of the Gulf Coast and the Caribbean islands were the inspiration for the composer of "Aurore Pradère."

Trinidadian singer Raymond Quevedo wrote and performed under the name of Atilla the Hun. Quevedo penned this tune in the early 1950s to protest the unfair treatment of black women in an annual beauty contest sponsored by the *Guardian,* a local newspaper. Although most of the contestants were women of color, the judges always gave first prize to a white woman. The practice outraged the black citizens of Trinidad, and Quevedo's biting social satire was popular throughout the island. This discriminatory practice has since been abandoned.

GUARDIAN BEAUTY CONTEST

By Atilla the Hun

I real – ly have to tell ___ you, Ev – e – lyn, girl, ___ it's on – ly

time you are ___ wast-ing. ___ I have to ___ Why all this hair-do and

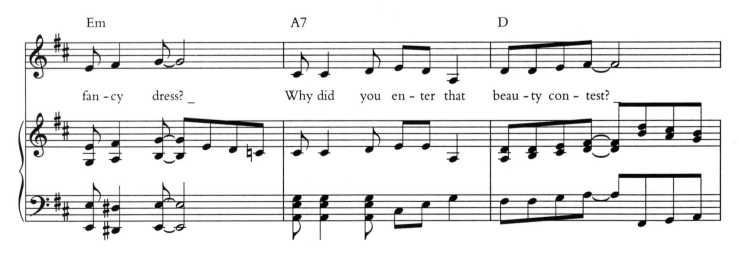

fan – cy dress? ___ Why did you en – ter that beau – ty con – test?

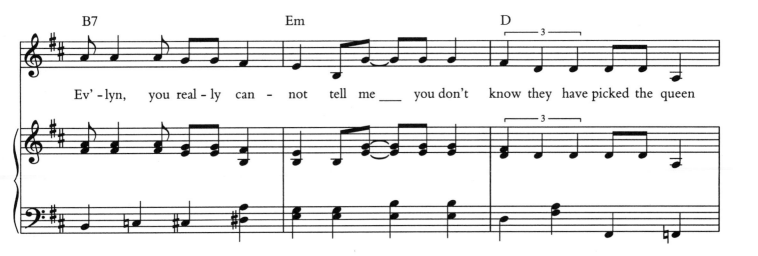

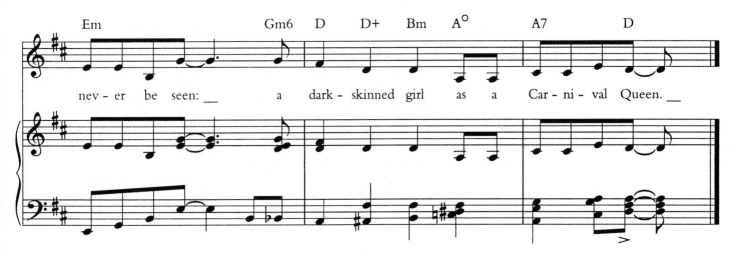

9

I have seen dark contestants in this country
Who were really symbols of beauty.
They were gorgeous and glamorous,
Some were even prettier than Venus.
With more personality than Myrna Loy
And greater attraction than Helen of Troy;
And all the passion of this world in their eyes –
Yet a flat - backed white woman gets the prize. *Chorus*

I, for one was never disappointed
From the time that the contest started.
I have seen many a brown - skinned miss
Who was the quintessence of loveliness.
But in the background hear a judge remark,
"She's really lovely, but she's too dark."
So it is with chagrin, despair and pain
You see another flat-back white woman get it again. *Chorus*

So it's time that our forces we enlist
And put an end to this stupidness.
Let us tell them all immediately
With protests from all over the whole country,
That when a beauty contest they are judging
There must be no question of color of skin.
And if no regard for our views is shown,
Let us leave this beauty contest alone. *Chorus*

Calypso songs are characterized by lively, drum-driven rhythms and often accompanied by flamboyant dancing. This has led many people to believe that the songs have no serious message to offer. The angry words to "Guardian Beauty Contest" and "The Commissioner's Report" tell a different story.

This is another song of protest by Atilla the Hun. During the 1930s, a group of unemployed workers led by a man named Butler staged a peaceful demonstration in Port of Spain, Trinidad. The police, however, claimed that the workers had started a riot. Armed officers attacked the group in full force, and several of the protesters were killed. After local residents complained that the police had used excessive force, a commission of inquiry was sent from England to investigate the incident. But the gentle reprimand that the guilty officers received did little to satisfy the anger of many local residents. Although Atilla's song earned him a brief jail sentence, it allowed the enraged islanders to express their feelings and eventually helped the composer get elected to the city council.

THE COMMISSIONER'S REPORT

By Atilla the Hun

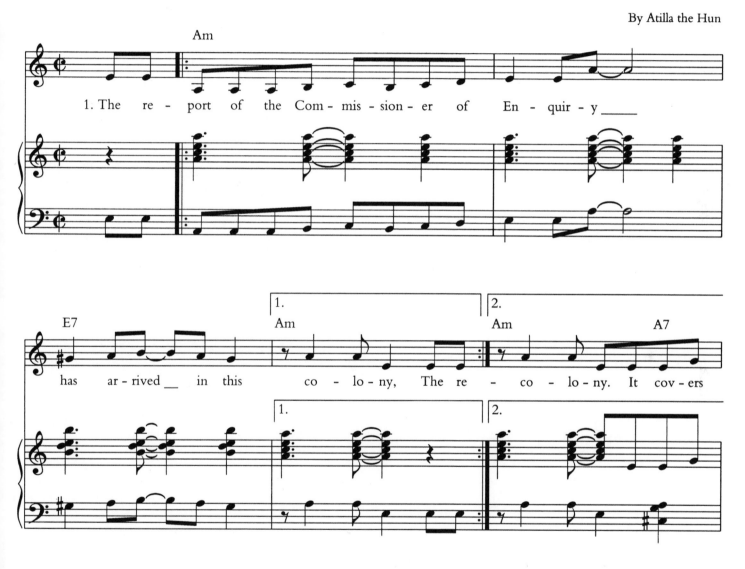

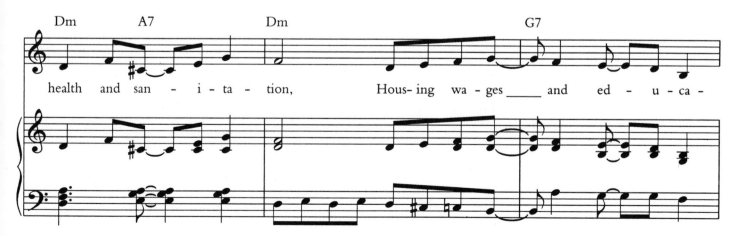

tion; It says that the ri - ots were __ ter - ri - ble, And de -clares that But - ler __

__ was re - spon - si - ble. 2. Be - cause of the ri - ots we had

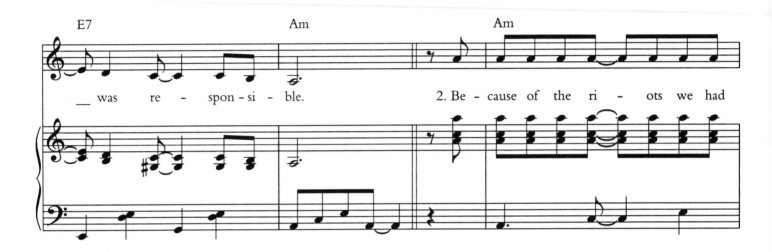

re - cent - ly, __ A com - mis - sion was sent __ from the moth- er coun- try, __ To in -

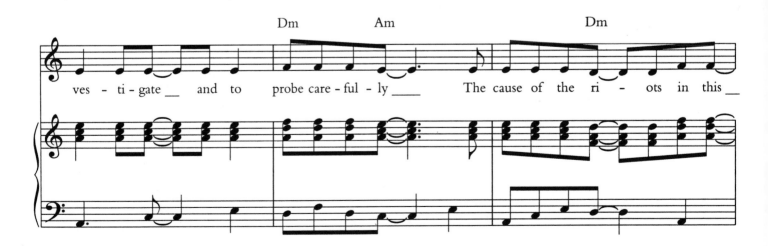

ves - ti - gate __ and to probe care - ful - ly ____ The cause of the ri - ots in this __

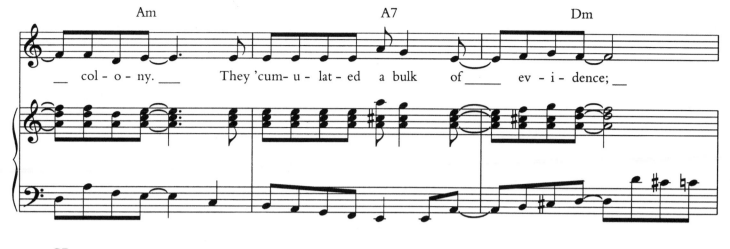

Sing verses 3, 4 and 5 to the melody of verse 2.

They criticized our ex-governor,
The well-known Mr. Jones, and his assistant, Fletcher.
And Howard Markville, they said that he
Had uttered speeches wrong to a marked degree.
They castigated M. Sivelly,
Our ex-colonial secretary.
But all of this just appears to me
An example of English diplomacy.

They said from the evidence they had,
That the riots started in Trinidad
By the hooligan element, under their leader –
A fanatic Negro named Butler,
Who uttered speeches inflammatory
And caused disorders in this colony.
The only time they said the police was wrong,
Was that they wait too long to shoot the people down!

A peculiar thing about this commission:
In ninety-two pages of dissertation,
There is no talk about exploitation
Of the worker, or of his tragic condition.
Read through the pages, there is no mention
Of capitalistic oppression;
Which leads one to entertain the thought
That maybe 'twas the very one-sided report.

The *criolla* is an urban dance in 6/8 time created by the Cuban bandleader Luis Casa Romero in 1909. Its rhythmic ambiguity—continually shifting from three beats to two—gives it that special feeling so common to much of Latin American music. "Criolla Carabalí" was recorded in New York City in 1928 by the Sexteto Habanero. In addition to their native Spanish, the group sang the song in the Nigerian language of Yoruba, a tribute to their African heritage.

CRIOLLA CARABALÍ

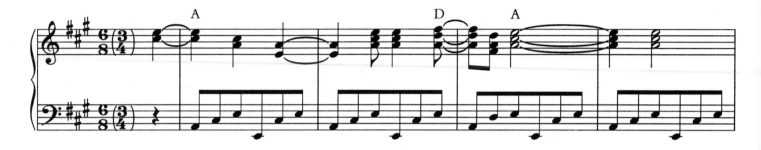

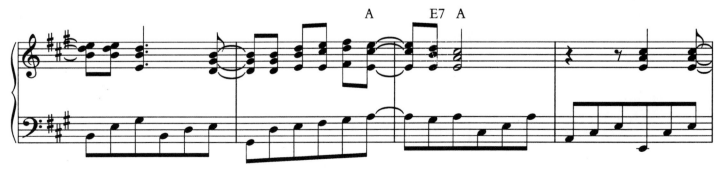

Life is a constant struggle for many of the inhabitants of the Caribbean islands. In some rural communities, the donkey is still the most convenient way to travel from village to village. Songs like "Criolla Carabalí" helped islanders forget their troubles and celebrate the natural beauty of their homeland.

This song refers to the celebrated romance between Edward VIII of England and Mrs. Wallis Simpson, a divorced socialite from Baltimore, Maryland. Edward assumed the English throne in January 1936, following the death of his father, King George V. Less than a year later, however, he abdicated his title in order to marry his American-born lover. The story made headlines around the world, and the couple became folk heroes for the millions of people who believed that love was more important than money or power. "I now quit altogether public affairs," Edward announced in his memorable farewell message on British radio, "and lay down my burden."

LOVE ALONE

Fine

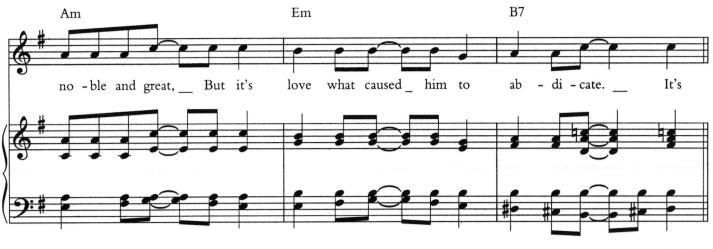

no -ble and great, __ But it's love what caused __ him to ab - di - cate. __ It's

D.S. al Fine

I know my mama she gonna grieve,
He said, "I cannot help but I am bound to leave."   *Chorus*

And he got the money and he got the talk,
And the fancy walk just to suit New York.   *Chorus*

You can take me throne, you can take me crown,
But leave me Miss Simpson to renown.   *Chorus*

Come a reel come a roll upon my mind,
I cannot leave Miss Simpson behind.   *Chorus*

If a plane and a ship don't carry me free,
I'll walk with Miss Simpson across the sea.   *Chorus*

On the 10th of December you heard the talk,
When he give the throne to the Duke of York.   *Chorus*

Then Baldwin want to break down his stand,
He said, "I'm giving up with my government."   *Chorus*

Now he's the victim of circumstance,
Now they live in the south of France.   *Chorus*

If you see Mrs. Simpson across the street,
You can guarantee she is a busy bee.   *Chorus*

Let the organ roll, let the church bell ring,
He said, "Good luck" to our second bachelor King.   *Chorus*

The poetic imagery of this haunting ballad is strongly reminiscent of the Negro spirituals of an earlier era. The familiar themes of rich and poor, life and death, the truth of the Bible, and a mother comforting a weeping child were all found in the songs of North American slaves. The lively, syncopated rhythms of "All My Trials," however, gives the song a distinctly West Indian flavor.

ALL MY TRIALS

If re-li-gion was a thing that mon-ey could buy,____

____ The rich would live ____ and the poor would die._____

Chorus

All _____ my trials, _ Lord,_____

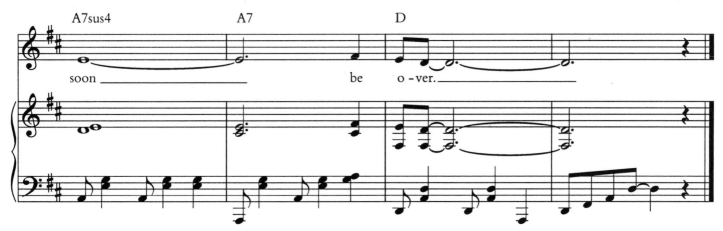

I had a little book, 'twas given to me
And every page spelled "Victory." *Chorus*

Hush little baby, don't you cry,
You know your mama was born to die. *Chorus*

This Haitian song was written in the Creole language, a mix of French, Spanish, and African languages that is only spoken in the West Indies and sections of the southern United States. *Feuille* (pronounced "fey") is the French word for leaf. In this song, it refers to the spirit of the leaves, invoked by a mother who hopes that they will save the life of her sick child. The *gan-gan* is the local medicine man, the only one who knows the secrets of the leaves.

FEUILLE-O

Feuille - o, ___ sau-vez la vie moin, __ nan mi - ser moin ye - o.
Feuille - o, ___ save my lit - tle one, __ save my pre - cious ba - by.

o. Pi - tit moin ma - lade, __ m' cou - ri caille gan - gan, __ si - mi -
by. Through the woods I run, __ just look-ing for *gan - gan*, __ Where is

lo, ___ Pi - tit moin ma - lade, __ m' cou - ri caille gan - gan, _ si li
he? ___ Through the woods I run, __ just look-ing for *gan - gan*, _ If he's

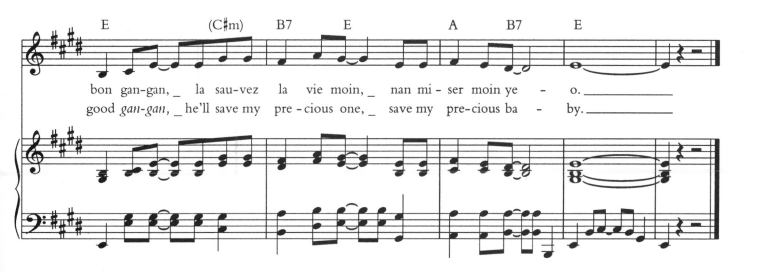

bon gan-gan, _ la sau-vez la vie moin, _ nan mi - ser moin ye - o. _____
good *gan-gan*, _ he'll save my pre-cious one, _ save my pre-cious ba - by. _____

The beauty of the Caribbean islands inspired many inhabitants to attribute mystical powers to nature. The distraught mother in "Feuille-O" hopes the spirit of the leaves will cure her sick child.

This is a Caribbean variation on the bawdy, old English ballad "Johnny Be Fair." The song deals humorously with the deceit and mistaken identity that lie at the heart of one Kingston family. As in the English tune, the song's comic solution undermines the very values that it seeks to uphold. The young protagonist is freed to pursue the joys of marriage and family life only because his parents have chosen to disregard those very values.

SHAME AND SCANDAL IN THE FAMILY

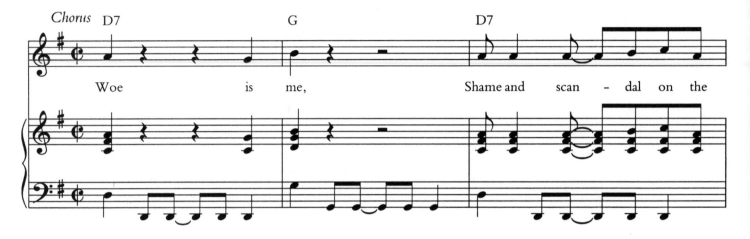

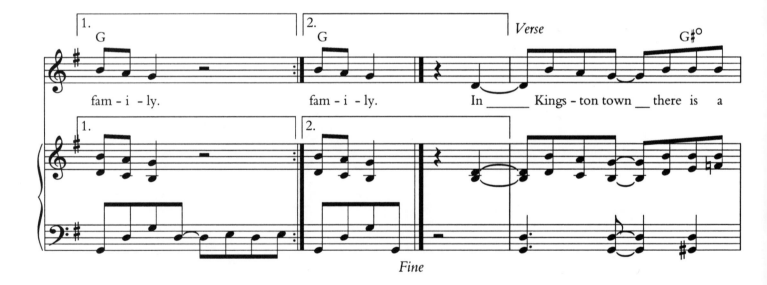

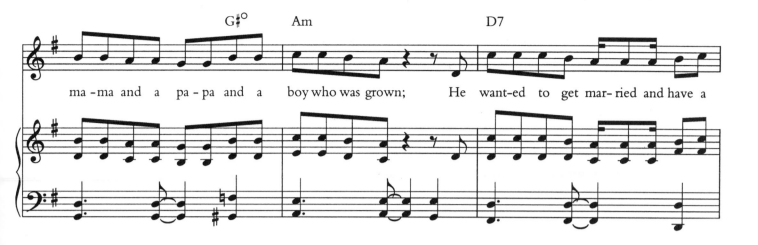

ma-ma and a pa-pa and a boy who was grown; He want-ed to get mar-ried and have a

wife of his own. He found a young girl who suit-ed him nice, He

went to his pa-pa to ask his ad-vice. His pa-pa said, "Son, I'll

have to say no. This girl is your sis-ter, but your ma-ma don't know." __

> D.C.

The week went by and the summer came down,
He took her to his mama to show her what he had found.
He went to his mama and covered his head.
He told his mama what his papa had said.
His mama she laughed and said, "Son, that's so.
Your daddy ain't your daddy, but your daddy don't know!"   *Chorus*

In the Georgia Sea Islands during the early 19th century, slave owners would often cast dead slaves into the open fields instead of giving them a proper burial. Set to the music of a West Indian miming dance, this song protests that barbaric practice. In the ritual that often accompanied the song, dancers formed a ring around a piece of cloth on the ground. The cloth represented the body of the dead slave, and the dancers fluttered their arms and swept their bodies over the cloth like the swarms of vultures that devoured the bodies in the fields.

THROW ME ANYWHERE

Don't care where you throw me,
In that old field,
Since my Jesus save me,
In that old field.

Don't care how you treat me,
In that old field,
Since King Jesus meet me,
In that old field.

Don't care how you do me,
In that old field,
Since King Jesus choose me,
In that old field.

Pete Seeger first introduced North Americans to this dance tune from the Bahamas in the 1950s. It originally had only one verse, but new verses were added as the song was introduced to audiences and performers. This is the kind of song that virtually rewrites itself every time somebody sings it. See what new verses you can add.

HEY LOLLY, LOLLY

Hey lol - ly, lol - ly, lol - ly, Hey lol - ly, lol - ly, lo. ___

Hey lol - ly, lol - ly, lol - ly, Hey lol - ly, lol - ly lo. ___

Fine

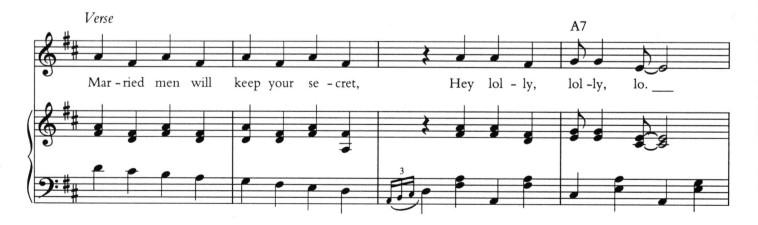

Mar - ried men will keep your se - cret, Hey lol - ly, lol - ly, lo. ___

Sin - gle boys will talk a - bout you, Hey lol - ly, lol - ly lo. ___

D

I have a girl, she's ten feet tall,
    Hey lolly, lolly lo.
Sleeps in the kitchen with her feet in the hall,
    Hey lolly, lolly lo.   *Chorus*

Everybody sing the chorus,
    Hey lolly, lolly lo.
Either you're against us or you're for us,
    Hey lolly, lolly lo.   *Chorus*

The purpose of this little song,
    Hey lolly, lolly lo.
Is to make up verses as you go along,
    Hey lolly, lolly lo.   *Chorus*

At a Carnival celebration in Port of Spain, Trinidad, the members of a local calypso band delight the crowd with their frenzied dancing and outrageous costumes.

This popular song is an adaptation of Psalm 137. It is a fairly typical example of the way in which a biblical text is used in West Indian music to express the deep feelings of slave descendants. In a shift away from the original meaning of the famous psalm, Zion represents Africa, and Babylon represents the New World to which African men and women have been dragged in chains.

RIVER OF BABYLON

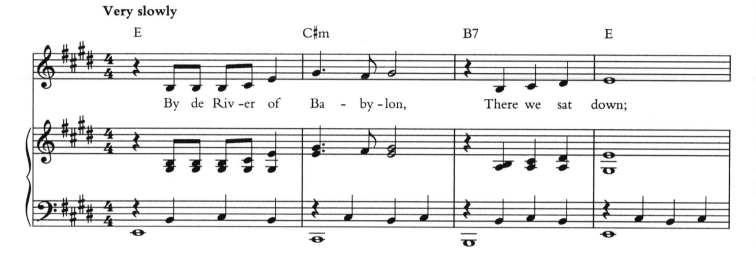

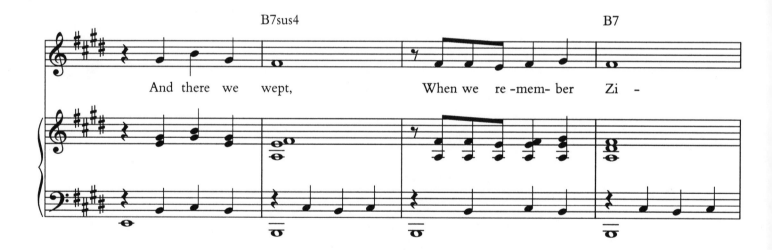

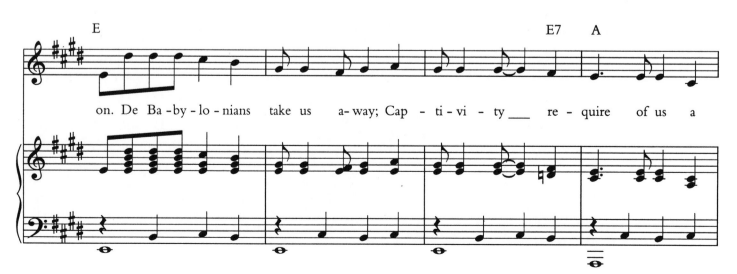

song, But how can I sing Ras-ta-fa-ri song in a strange land?

The sea is an ever-present influence in the songs of the West Indian islands. Many of the islands' inhabitants spend much of their lives on the waters of the Caribbean, working as sailors or fishermen. The sailor and captain in the song are two such men, and their conflict is over an unpaid debt. The song contains echoes of the English sailor's song "Blow the Man Down" in the phrase, "As soon as that packet was clear of the bar . . . the mate knocked me down with the end of the spar." The refrain, "pay me my money down," is substituted for, "to me way, hey, blow the man down."

PAY ME MY MONEY DOWN

Pay me,__ oh, pay me,__ Pay me my mon-ey down,__

Pay me or go to jail,__ Pay me my mon-ey down. _

Fine

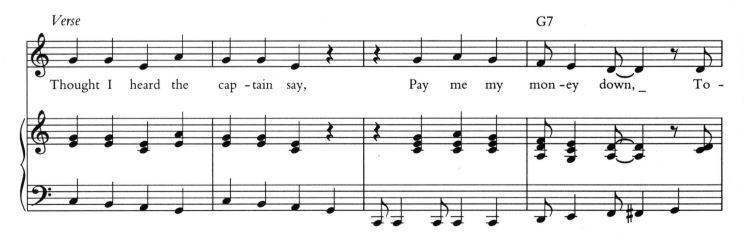

Verse

Thought I heard the cap-tain say, Pay me my mon-ey down,__ To-

mor-row is our sail-ing day, __ Pay me my mon-ey down. __

I wish I was Mister Howard's son,
Pay me my money down.
Sit in the house and drink all the rum,
Pay me my money down. *Chorus*

The very next day we cleared the bar,
Pay me my money down.
He knocked me down with the end of a spar,
Pay me my money down. *Chorus*

I wish I was Mister Steven's son,
Pay me my money down.
Sit in the shade and watch all the work done,
Pay me my money down. *Chorus*

There's lots more verses to this song,
Pay me my money down.
But I guess we better be moving along,
Pay me my money down. *Chorus*

Fruit handlers on a New Orleans banana boat load their heavy cargo from sunup to sundown. "Pay Me My Money Down" tells the story of a quarrel between one of these workers and the captain of his ship.

This song reflects the Caribbean tradition of *Kumina*, an African-Jamaican way of life practiced mainly on the islands of Jamaica and St. Thomas. With roots in the Congo region of West Africa, Kumina involves spirit possession, ancestor worship, ritual dance, drumming, and music. "Lion Deh Pon Road" was first recorded in Jamaica in 1967 by popular Kumina drummer Lovelace MacFarlane. It is in Jamaican Creole, a Caribbean English rooted in African languages, Spanish, and English.

LION DEH PON ROAD

D.C. al Fine

'Memba muma tell yuh seh, fe mine hard 'aise oh,
'Memba muma tell yuh seh, fe mine hard 'aise oh.
Tan to yuh wud dahta, lan to yuh wud,
'Memba muma tell yuh seh, fe mine hard 'aise.

'Member mama tells you that these are hard days,
'Member mama tells you that these are hard days.
Then you will go daughter, then you will go,
'Member mama tells you that these are hard days.

Repeat first verse

There are unmistakable echoes of the North American ballad "Frankie and Johnny" in this song of a lover's revenge. In "Frankie and Johnny," Frankie kills her boyfriend Johnny because "he was doing her wrong." "Delia" gives no specific motive for Tony's crime, though it seems clear that she was probably doing him wrong as well.

DELIA

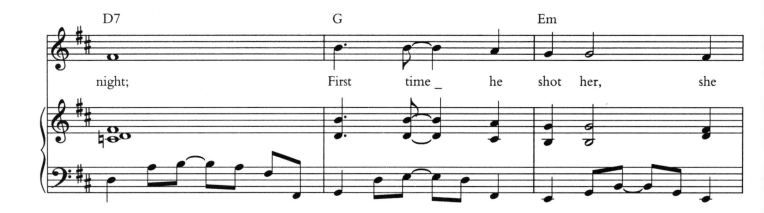

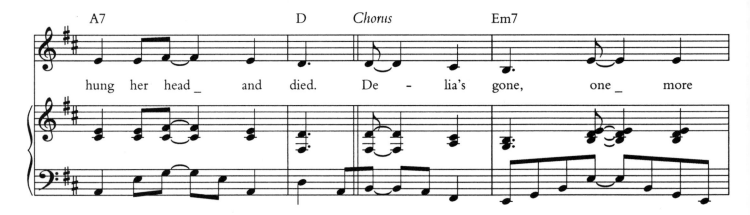

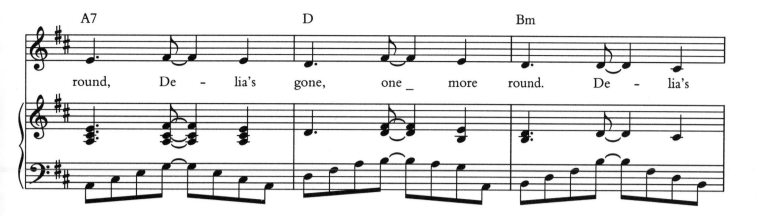

round, De - lia's gone, one _ more round. De - lia's

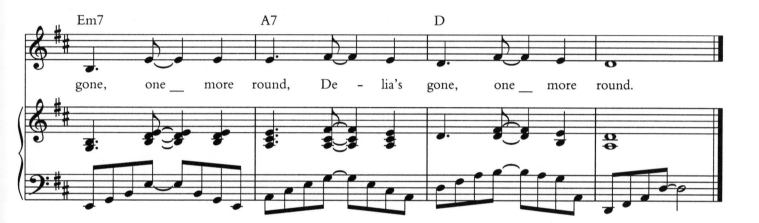

gone, one _ more round, De - lia's gone, one _ more round.

Send for the doctor— the doctor came too late.
Send for the minister to lay out Delia straight. *Chorus*

Delia, oh, Delia, where you been so long?
Everybody's talking about poor Delia's dead and gone. *Chorus*

Rubber-tired carriage – old-time broken hack
Took poor Delia to the graveyard but didn't bring her back. *Chorus*

Popularized in the 1950s by singer Harry Belafonte, this may be the best-known calypso song in the United States. With its haunting call and response, the song perfectly captures the wistful longing of the dock workers on the night shift, singing together as they load the bananas onto the boat.

DAY-O

make me shiv - er, Day-light break _ and I wan-na go home.

Load bananas bunch by bunch,
 Daylight break and I wanna go home.
Skipped my supper, lost my lunch,
 Daylight break and I wanna go home.   *Chorus*

When morning comes my work is done,
 Daylight break and I wanna go home.
Sleep all day till the setting sun,
 Daylight break and I wanna go home.   *Chorus*

Kissed my wife 'bout a quarter to eight,
 Daylight come and I wanna go home.
Back on the river—can't be late,
 Daylight come and I wanna go home.   *Chorus*

The most popular calypso song in the United States, "Day-O" became a hit for singer Harry Belafonte in the 1950s.

The *calinda* mentioned in the chorus of this satirical Creole song is a dance with a long, controversial history. In the early 19th century, calinda songs were sung in Trinidad to accompany the *bois-bataille* (stick fight), a sort of ritualistic game in which dueling with hardwood sticks was performed in time to the beating of drums. After the Emancipation of 1838, calinda was taken into the Carnival, to the distaste and resentment of the upper classes. There were a number of attempts by the police to suppress the tradition, finally resulting in a major confrontation and riot in 1881. After that, the calinda went underground—to be practiced in the back rooms and alleyways of the island's urban areas—where it continues to this day.

MICHIÉ PRÉVAL

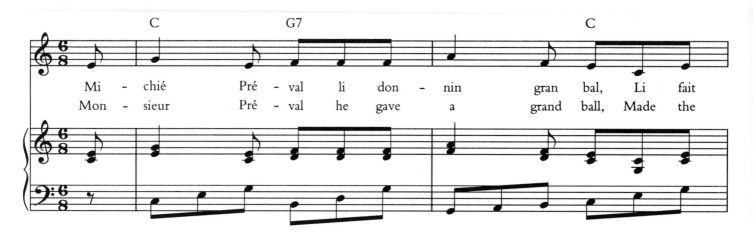

Mi - chié Pré - val li don - nin gran bal, Li fait
Mon - sieur Pré - val he gave a grand ball, Made the

nèg' pa - yer pou sau - ter in pé. Dan - sé ca - lin - da, bou -
black folks pay to en - joy them - selves. O, dance ca - lin - da, bou -

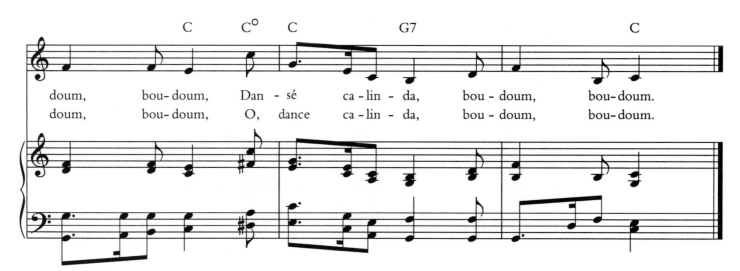

doum, bou - doum, Dan - sé ca - lin - da, bou - doum, bou - doum.
doum, bou - doum, O, dance ca - lin - da, bou - doum, bou - doum.

Michié Préval li té capitaine bal,
So cocher Louis té maite cérémonie.   *Chorus*

Dans léquirie la yavé gran gala,
Mo cré choual layé té bien étonné.   *Chorus*

Yavé des négresse belle passé maitresse,
Yé volé bébelle dans l'ormoire mamzelle.   *Chorus*

"Comment, Sazou, té volé mo cuilotte?"
"Non, no maîtr', mo di vous zes prend bottes."   *Chorus*

Ala maîtr' geole li trouvé si drole,
Li dit, "Moin aussi mo fé bal ici."   *Chorus*

Yé prend maîtr' Préval yé metté le prison,
Pasque li donnin bal pou volé nous l'arzan.   *Chorus*

Monsieur Préval danced around the hall,
And his coachman, Louis, did make the calls.   *Chorus*

'Twas in the stable the gala blazed,
I'm sure the horses were all amazed.   *Chorus*

The women were prettier than their mistresses,
Because they stole their mistresses' dresses.   *Chorus*

"What's this, Sazou, you stole my pants?"
"No, Master, I borrowed your boots to dance."   *Chorus*

The jailor said when he did come,
"I'll join the dance and have some fun."   *Chorus*

He then took Préval and locked him away,
For giving the ball to steal our pay.   *Chorus*

Convicts on the island prison of Carera in Trinidad sang this song around the end of the 19th century to protest the desperate conditions under which they were forced to live and work. Though only a fragment of the song has survived, it reveals a great deal about the history of West Indian music. The song dates from an earlier period in which music was known as "cariso." The French words, *sans d'humanité* (without humanity), hint at the influence of French settlers on the island's culture.

DOUBLE DRILL

Down in the met - tle heap is to hear them weep, is to see them

beat. Down in the met - tle heap is to hear them

weep, is to see them beat on top the hill. See them

driv-ing dou-ble drill, On top the hill, on top the

hill. See them driv - ing dou - ble drill,

Sans d'hu-ma - ni - té! On top the té!

Calypso music plays a central role in almost all of the islands' celebrations and festivities. Here a group of local citizens dance through the streets of Nassau in the Bahamas as part of the island's Independence Day parade.

The humorous concept of "dry weather houses" expressed in this Jamaican song has its counterpart in the classic American bluegrass song "The Arkansas Traveller." In the latter tune, a wise old farmer shrugs off the unsolicited advice of a city slicker. The young man instructs the farmer to repair his leaky roof on the next sunny day. "My cabin never leaks when it doesn't rain," the old man retorts.

DRY WEATHER HOUSES

One Mon-day morn-ing, a land-lord went to a ten-ant to get some

rent; But the ten-ant say, "Lis-ten, __ me no fool, Me no pay no

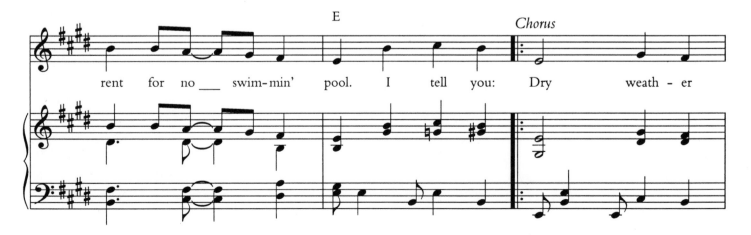

rent for no __ swim-min' pool. I tell you: Dry weath-er

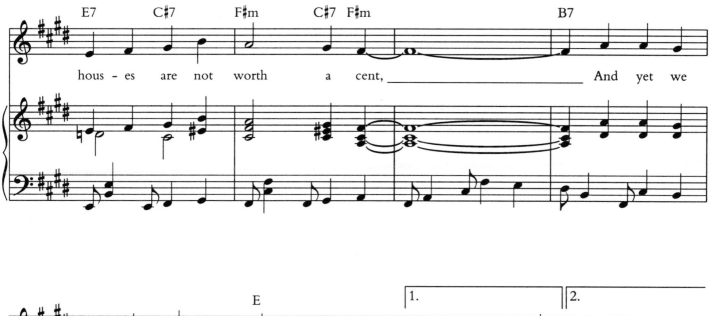

hous - es are not worth a cent, _____ And yet we

have to pay so much for rent!"___ (sing it out now) ___

Look at the room you rent me to live,
The whole of the roof is just like a sieve,
If it rain at night and I sleep too sound,
So help me king, I sure would 'a drowned.
I tell you . . .   *Chorus*

Some of the rooms, the way them so small,
You can't even turn 'round in them at all;
When you want to turn you gotta go outside,
Turn your back and go back inside.
I tell you . . .   *Chorus*

Folklorists Alan Lomax and Mary Elizabeth Barnicle collected this Bahamian sailor's song in Nassau in 1935 from the singing of Henry Lundy. Built around the refrain, "Way oh, Susianna," the song blends the repetitiveness of a British chantey, or sailor's song, with a gently syncopated, West Indian melody.

'ROUND THE BAY OF MEXICO

Then, 'round the Bay of Mex-i-co,__ Way oh,

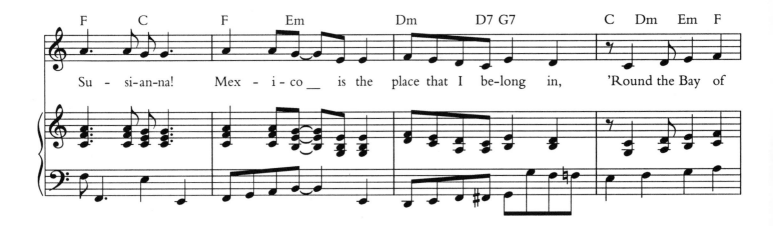

Su-si-an-na! Mex-i-co__ is the place that I be-long in, 'Round the Bay of

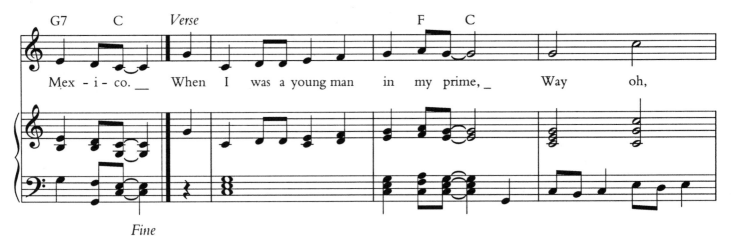

Mex-i-co.__ When I was a young man in my prime,_ Way oh,

Su - si- an- na! I'd love those pret - ty girls two __ at a time, ____

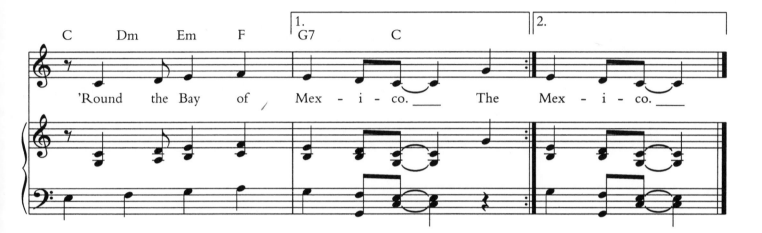

'Round the Bay of Mex - i - co. ____ The Mex - i - co. ____

The reason those girls they love me so,
    Way oh, Susianna!
Because I don't tell everything that I know,
    'Round the Bay of Mexico. *Chorus*

Them Nassau girls ain't got no combs,
    Way oh, Susianna!
They comb their hair with whipper-back bones,
    'Round the Bay of Mexico. *Chorus*

The bustling market in Kingston, Jamaica has been made famous by a number of calypso songs. The song "Jamaica Farewell" contains a colorful description of what life used to be like on the streets of Kingston: "Down at the market you can hear ladies cry out as on their heads they bear acki, rice. Salt fish is nice, and the rum is fine any time of the year." Like "Jamaica Farewell," "Let Me Go Down" expresses a gentle nostalgia for an island paradise that probably never really existed.

LET ME GO DOWN

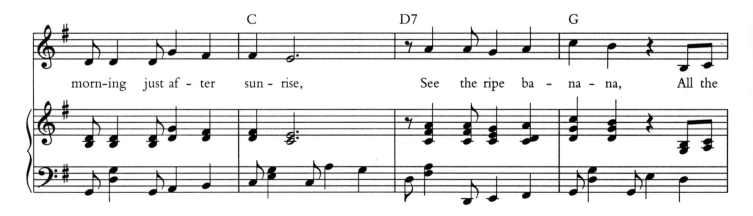

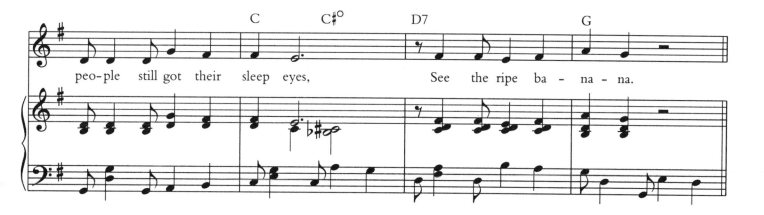

peo-ple still got their sleep eyes, See the ripe ba - na - na.

By the time that the clock strikes seven,
   See the ripe banana,
You might think that you've entered heaven,
   See the ripe banana. *Chorus*

For the smells, they are so delicious,
   See the ripe banana,
You can sample a hundred dishes,
   See the ripe banana. *Chorus*

There is acki and sweet potato,
   See the ripe banana,
Shrimp and chicken and ripe tomato,
   See the ripe banana. *Chorus*

You'll see fishermen, you'll see farmers,
   See the ripe banana,
You'll see jugglers and snake charmers,
   See the ripe banana. *Chorus*

What would I not give just to be there,
   See the ripe banana,
Just to have one more cup of tea there,
   See the ripe banana. *Chorus*

A pair of Jamaican peasants slowly make their way to the Kingston market. The sights, sounds, and smells of the city were festive rewards for those who were willing to make the long journey.

With their intricate rhymes and bouncing rhythms, calypso songs serve as perfect vehicles for
social protest. Rupert Grant, known in calypso circles as the Lord Invader, wrote this angry song
in 1946. The song's startlingly direct lyrics reflect the experiences of black servicemen returning
home from World War II. Even after risking their lives in the war, they found that they still faced
racial discrimination in their homelands.

GOD MADE US ALL

By Rupert Grant

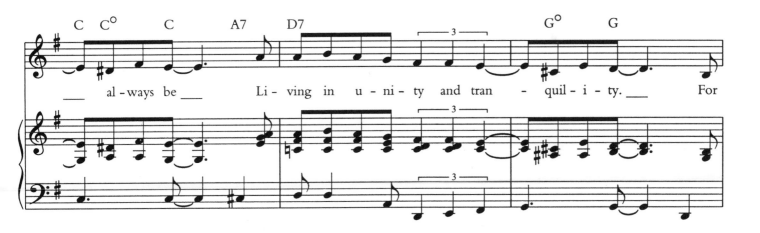

al-ways be ___ Li-ving in u-ni-ty and tran - quil-i-ty. ___ For

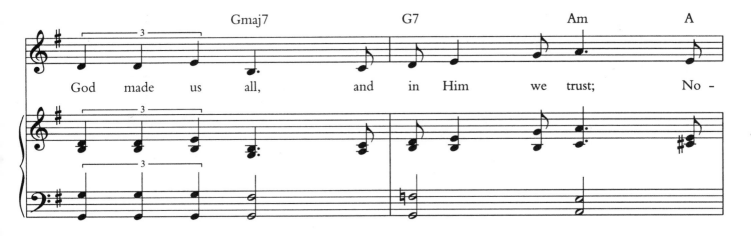

God made us all, and in Him we trust; No -

bod - y in the world is bet - ter than us.

Listen what I am outlining to you:
Negroes fought in World Wars One and Two.
Some lose their lives, others lose a hand,
We fought gallantly for the United Nations.
So if we Negroes are good enough to fight,
I don't see why we can't have our equal right,
　　For God made us all, and in Him we trust,
　　Nobody in this world is better than us.

We ought to unite with one another,
As the scripture say, to love thy neighbor;
If you are a Jew or an Italian,
A Negro or a subject of Great Britain,
This is what I want you to realize:
Six feet of earth make us all of one size,
　　For God made us all, and in Him we trust,
　　Nobody in this world is better than us.

I heard this speaking of democracy;
That is only diplomacy and hypocrisy.
It is about time this should be cut out,
The way the Negroes are treated down South.
In my opinion it's a burning shame,
Like they want to bring back slavery again,
　　For God made us all, and in Him we trust,
　　Nobody in this world is better than us.

It is not always possible to pinpoint the exact origin of a particular song. Folksinger Pete Seeger believes that this tuneful American folk song has West Indian roots. The song's invocation of sea and sun certainly suggests warmer climates and sunnier vistas. Willie's resurrection by the golden sun, after having been "drownded," reinforces that feeling. In any case, this beautiful song is perfect for group singing.

DEEP BLUE SEA

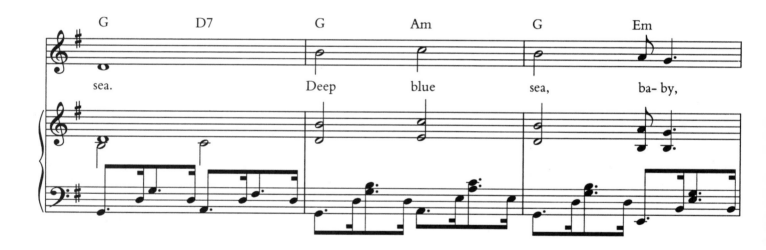

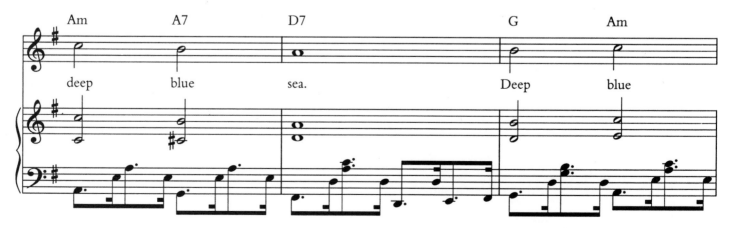

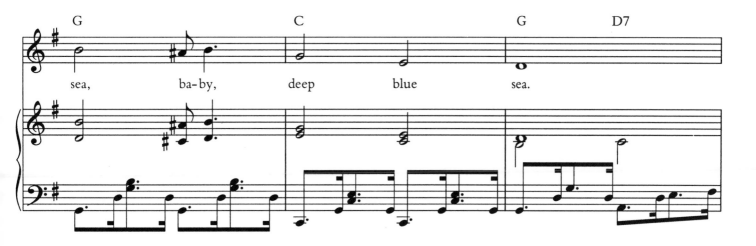

sea, ba-by, deep blue sea.

It was Wil-lie what got drown-ded in the

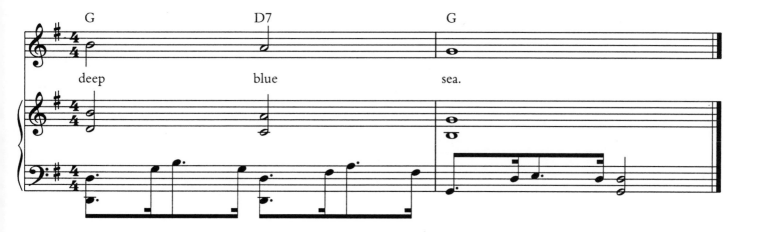

deep blue sea.

Dig his grave with a silver spade, *(3 times)*
It was Willie what got drownded in the deep blue sea.   *Chorus*

Lower him down with a golden chain, *(3 times)*
It was Willie what got drownded in the deep blue sea.   *Chorus*

Golden sun bring him back again, *(3 times)*
It was Willie what got drownded in the deep blue sea.   *Chorus*

This song was first sung by the Bahamian singer Blake Alphonso Higgs, or Blind Blake. It commemorates a deadly hurricane that swept through the Caribbean islands in 1929. The tiny island communities are vulnerable to all types of natural disasters, and floods and storms have always been important themes for West Indian ballad singers.

RUN COME SEE JERUSALEM

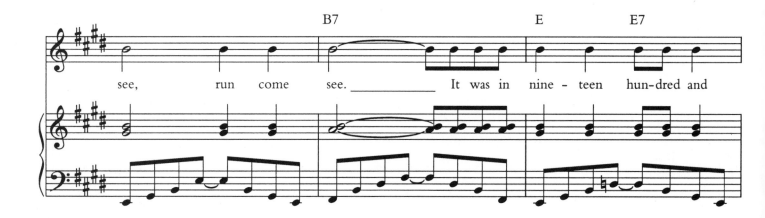

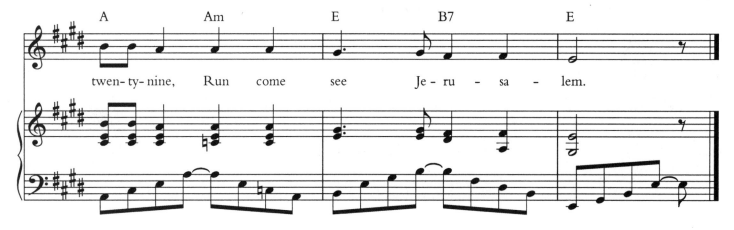

That day they were talking 'bout a storm in the islands . . .   (2)

That day there were three ships leaving out the harbor . . .   (2)

It was the *Ethel,* the *Myrtle* and the *Pretoria* . . .   (2)

They were bound for the island of Andros . . .   (2)

The *Pretoria* was out on the ocean . . .   (2)

Right then it was a big sea built up in the northwest . . .   (2)

My God, when the first wave hit the *Pretoria* . . .   (2)

My God, there were thirty-three souls on the water . . .   (2)

My God, now George Brown he was the captain . . .   (2)

He said, "Come now, witness your judgment" . . .   (2)

There'll be no more waiting on Andros . . .   (2)

"Run Come See Jerusalem" tells the story of how vulnerable the islanders are to hurricane and flood. Most of the time, however, the weather is fine. Here the residents of Kingston, Jamaica, enjoy a typically sunny day at the Jubilee Market.

The bitter sentiments expressed in this song seem to be universal. The song was written by the Trinidadian singer Neville Marcano, also known as the Tiger. A popular calypso performer who often wrote songs about oppression and other social problems, Marcano also wrote the song "Workers' Appeal," included later in this collection.

MONEY IS KING

By The Tiger

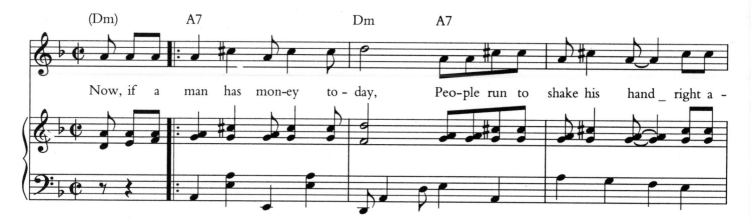

Now, if a man has mon-ey to-day, Peo-ple run to shake his hand_ right a-

way. Yes, if a day. He can com-mit mur-der and get off free,_

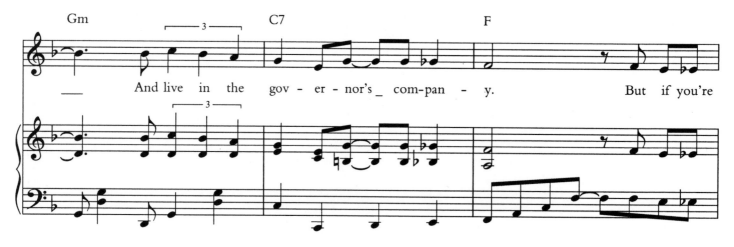

And live in the gov-er-nor's_ com-pan-y. But if you're

poor, why God help you, _ E-ven a dog is bet-ter than you.

Now a man with money can go to the store.
The boss will run to shake his hand at the door.
Call ten clerks to write down everything—
Suits, hats, whisky, and diamond rings!
They will take it to your home on a motorbike,
You can pay for it whenever you like;
Not a soul will tell you a thing,
They know very well that Money is King!

Even a dog can run around and pick up bones,
Salt fish, codfish, meat, and pone;
If it's a good breed and not too wild,
People will take it and mind it like a child.
But a hungry man goes out to beg,
They will set the bulldog behind his leg.
So most of you will agree, it is true —
Even a dog is better than you.

The beauty of the islands and the festive spirit of the marketplaces often hide a darker story. Many dock workers, fishermen, and cane farmers can barely make enough to survive. "If you're poor," go the lyrics to "Money Is King," "even a dog is better than you."

Al Wood, a young songwriter of West Indian descent, was living in the Bronx, New York, when he wrote this song in 1951. Wood was a friend and neighbor of the author of this book, and the two often performed together at hootenannies and other folk-song concerts. Audiences were always moved by the intense imagery of this powerful song.

GENOCIDE

By Albert Wood

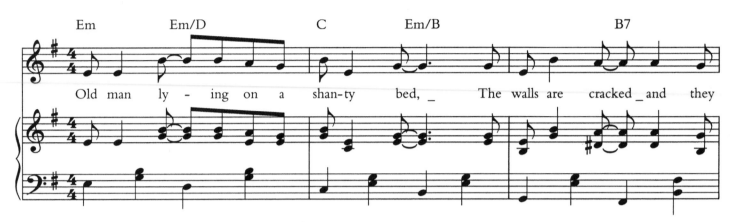

Old man ly - ing on a shan - ty bed, _ The walls are cracked _ and they

lean. Look real close, _ he's not old at all, _ But a youth of on - ly six -

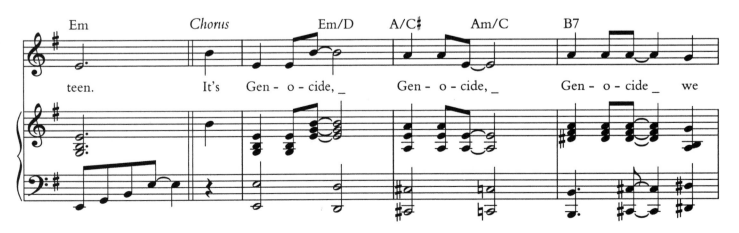

teen. It's Gen - o - cide, _ Gen - o - cide, _ Gen - o - cide _ we

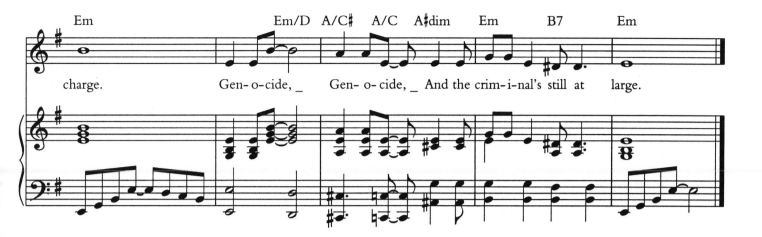

charge. Gen- o- cide, _ Gen- o- cide, _ And the crim-i-nal's still at large.

Young woman bleeding in a cotton field,
Her head's been broken, her privates revealed,
The rapists laughed and they strolled away,
What a terrible price the black women pay.   *Chorus*

Young man dying on a shanty bed,
He coughs, his spittle is streaked with red,
The midwife sighs, there's nothing she can do,
No hospital, no doctor, his life is through.   *Chorus*

Two frightened black youths hiding in the dark,
The Klansmen cursing and the hound-dogs bark,
White woman claimed that she was raped today,
And so a gory, bloody lynching is under way.   *Chorus*

Macio's dead, you know the reason why,
He heard he could vote so he went to try,
But they shot him down with this retort,
Black man vote and his life is short.   *Chorus*

Now you've heard of my people being beaten and lynched,
But they rise back up and don't give an inch,
And we're fighting back, this we say with pride,
Black and white stopping Genocide!   *Chorus*

This song was written during the Great Depression of the 1930s. The song's composer, Neville Marcano, also known as The Tiger, was among the most popular calypso singers during the 1940s and 1950s. Marcano traveled frequently from his home in Port of Spain, Trinidad, to New York City, where he made records that sold widely in both Trinidad and the United States. As in another of his compositions, "Money Is King," included earlier in this collection, Marcano's songs often addressed social problems.

WORKERS' APPEAL

By The Tiger

An-y-where you go you must meet _ peo-ple sad; They search _ for em-

ploy-ment, none _ can be had. An-y-where you had. They start to

drop down dead _ in the street; No-where to sleep and noth-ing to eat, So,

kind-heart-ed em-ploy-ers, I ap-peal now to you: Give us some work to do.

We are not asking for equality,
To rank with the rich in society,
To visit their homes in their motorcars,
Or to go to their clubs and smoke their cigars.
We are asking for a living wage
To exist now and provide for old age.
Our kindhearted employers, I appeal now to you,
Give us some work to do.

Many a day, persons haven't a meal.
They were too decent to beg, too honest to steal.
They went looking for work mostly everywhere,
But saw signboard marked "No hands wanted here."
The government should work the wastelands and hills,
Build houses, factories and mills,
Reduce taxation and then we would be really
Emancipated from slavery.

The legislators only quarrel and fret
About unemployment but haven't relieved us yet.
There is no visions that we can see
To take us out from tribulations and misery.
We can't fight physically for we wouldn't prevail
On account of ammunition, cruel laws and jail.
But every man was born to be free
From this oppression and tyrannic slavery.

While tourists and plantation owners enjoy the tropical scenery, local workers labor beneath the relentless sun. "Workers' Appeal" pays tribute to the hard lives of those who work the islands' docks and fields.

This lively tune has been sung by countless North American performers, including the Beach Boys, who made the song popular in the 1960s. With its delightful melody, balladlike story, and lively chorus, it is the favorite West Indian song of many folksingers.

THE SLOOP JOHN B.

We come on the sloop *John* B. My grand - fa - ther and

me. 'Round Nas - sau town we ____ did roam. ____

____ Drink - ing all night, _____ we got _ in a fight, _____

I feel so break up, _____ I want to go home. _____

Chorus:
So hoist up the *John B.* sails,
See how the mainsail sets,
Send for the captain ashore, let me go home.
Let me go home, let me go home,
I feel so break up, I want to go home.

The first mate, oh, he got drunk,
Broke up the people's trunk,
Constable had to come and take him away.
Sheriff Johnstone, please leave me alone,
I feel so break up, I want to go home.   *Chorus*

The poor cook, oh, he got fits,
Ate up all of the grits.
Then he took and threw away all of the corn.
Sheriff Johnstone, please leave me alone,
This is the worst trip I ever been on.   *Chorus*

This Creole slave song was first published in *Slave Songs of the United States* in 1867. The song pokes fun at a dandy, or a man in fancy dress, who is putting on airs for the women in the crowd. The song was often accompanied by a high-stepping dance or *bamboula,* taken from a Guinea word for drum. West African drums served as the basic rhythmic support for many of the early slave dances. The banjo is also of African origin.

Musieu Bainjo

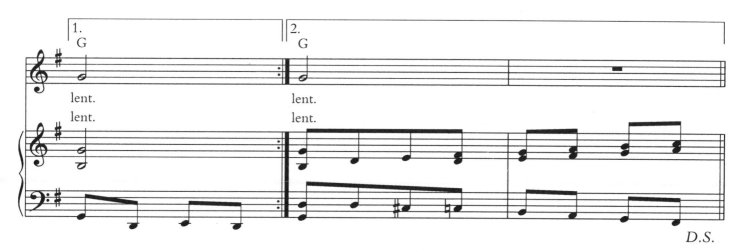

D.S.

Each verse has the same lyrics, except for the bracketed words which change as the song progresses.

Voyez ses gants jaunes . . .	See his yellow gloves . . .
Bottes qui fé *crin, crin* . . .	Boots that go *squeak, squeak* . . .
Bague de diamant . . .	Great big diamond ring . . .
Montre d'argent . . .	Fancy silver watch . . .

The lively music, frenzied dances, and colorful costumes of calypso reflect the various traditions that have been combined in the music.

Jerry Silverman is one of America's most prolific authors of music books. He has a B.S. degree in music from the City College of New York and an M.A. in musicology from New York University. He has authored some 100 books dealing with various aspects of guitar, banjo, violin, and fiddle technique, as well as numerous songbooks and arrangements for other instruments. He teaches guitar and music to children and adults and performs in folk-song concerts before audiences of all ages.

Kenneth B. Clark received a Ph.D. in social psychology from Columbia University and is the author of numerous books and articles on race and education. His books include *Prejudice and Your Child*, *Dark Ghetto*, and *Pathos of Power*. Long noted as an authority on segregation in schools, his work was cited by the U.S. Supreme Court in its decision in the historic *Brown v. Board of Education of Topeka* case in 1954. Dr. Clark, Distinguished Professor of Psychology Emeritus at the City University of New York, is the president of Kenneth B. Clark & Associates, a consulting firm specializing in personnel matters, race relations, and affirmative action programs.